Famous Tales
of

Gilbert Shelton

Knockabout

Famous Tales of Fat Freddy's Cat

by Gilbert Shelton
© 1994 Gilbert Shelton
Published by Knockabout Comics,
10 Acklam Road,
London W10 5QZ.
The moral right of the author has been asserted.
A CIP catalogue record for this book
is available from the British Library.
Designed by Rian 'Chinsome' Hughes
This edition not for sale in the USA or Canada

Send for our free illustrated catalogue

ISBN 086166 115 X
Printed in England by the Bath Press

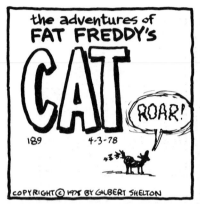

the adventures of FAT FREDDY'S CAT

COPYRIGHT © 1978 BY GILBERT SHELTON

ME OUT?

C'MON! GO OUT!

HMMMN! I HADN'T CONSIDERED THE POSSIBILITY OF IT BEING COLD OUTSIDE!

GO! GO!

NO! I CHANGED MY MIND!

SLAM!

YAGGGHHH! EVEN THE GROUND IS COLD!

HOP — HOP

HOW CAN YOU SIT DOWN ON THE GROUND LIKE THAT?

OH, IT'S NOT BAD AFTER YOU GET USED TO IT!

the adventures of
FAT FREDDY's
CAT

170
1/21/77

COPYRIGHT © 1977 BY GILBERT SHELTON

TELL US SOME HISTORY, UNCLE F.!

WHAT WOULD YOU LIKE TO KNOW?

WHAT WAS IT LIKE BEFORE THE HUMAN BEINGS CAME AND CAUGHT AND ENSLAVED ALL THE CATS?

YOU'VE GOT IT BACKWARDS! THE CATS WERE THE ONES THAT INITIATED THIS SYMBIOTIC RELATIONSHIP WITH THE PEOPLE!

BUT WHY, UNCLE F.??

SO THAT THE CATS WOULD BE ABLE TO GET MILK FROM COWS WITHOUT GETTING THEIR HEADS STEPPED ON!

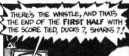

the adventures of
FAT FREDDY'S
CAT

HOW AM I GOING TO GET HOME? IT MUST BE CLEAR ACROSS THE CITY!

AH! DOGS ARE SUPPOSED TO HAVE A KEEN SENSE OF DIRECTION AND AN INSTINCTIVE KNOWLEDGE OF WHERE THEY ARE AT ALL TIMES!

CAN YOU TELL ME HOW TO GET HOME?

WELL, WHERE DO YOU LIVE?

2416 TRASHVIEW CRESCENT, APT. D.

NOPE, SORRY.

MAYBE I PHRASED THAT WRONG.

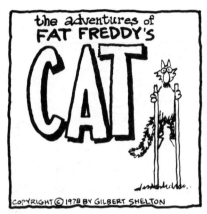

the adventures of
FAT FREDDY'S **CAT**

HOME SWEET HOME

WHEN YOU MOVE YOUR **CAT** INTO A **NEW HOUSE**, HOW DO YOU KEEP HIM FROM **RUNNING AWAY**?

WELL, FIRST YOU POUR HIM A **LARGE BOWL** OF **FOOD**...

FIDO

...THEN LOCK FOOD AND CAT IN KITCHEN UNTIL THE CAT **FORGETS** HIS **OLD** HOME!

CLICK.

HOW LONG DOES **THAT** TAKE?

ABOUT **THREE TENTHS** OF A **SECOND**.

the adventures of
FAT FREDDY's
CAT

©1991 BY GILBERT SHELTON

AH, HOW **PEACEFUL** IT IS TO STROLL THROUGH THE CITY IN THE EARLY MORNING HOURS BEFORE ALL THE **PEOPLE** BEGIN TO WAKE UP!

THE **STREETS** ARE **TOTALLY DEVOID** OF **MOTOR VEHICLES!**

THERE'S A TINY **TRAFFIC ISLAND** THAT I NEVER NOTICED BEFORE OUT IN THE MIDDLE OF THIS INTERSECTION! I THINK I'LL **VISIT** IT!

IT'S LIKE BEING ON A LITTLE **TROPICAL ISLAND** IN THE MIDDLE OF THE **OCEAN!**

the adventures of
FAT FREDDY's

CAT

192   4-24-78

WANT TO SEE A HUMOROUS ONE-ACT DRAMA? WATCH!

MEOW!

SCRATCH

(MOAN!) COME ON IN, PUSSYCAT! YOU WOKE ME UP WITH YOUR PITIABLE MEOWING AND SCRATCHING!

WELL, DON'T JUST SIT THERE! COME ON IN! I'M FREEZING MY BUNS OFF! COME IN! HEEERE KITTY KITTY KITTY!

#@☆%!

SLAM

CLAP CLAP CLAP CLAP CLAP

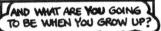

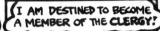

the adventures of
FAT FREDDY's
CAT

WRIT OF HABEAS CORPUS

MEYOW!

YOU CAN'T GO OUTSIDE, PUSSYCAT! YOU'LL JUST GET ALL **DIRTY**!

THAT **SADIST**! HE'S KEEPING ME LOCKED UP IN HERE FOR HIS OWN AMUSEMENT!

HA HA HA! WHAT ARE YOU GOING TO DO, KITTY? NOTIFY THE S.P.C.A.?

YOWL! CRY!

S.P.C.A., HECK! I'M CALLING THE **A.C.L.U.**!

the adventures of
FAT FREDDY'S
CAT

©1989 BY GILBERT SHELTON

THERE HE GOES **AGAIN**!

THAT **SAME DOG** COMES ALONG AT THE **SAME TIME** EVERY DAY AND **SHITS** ON THE SAME PLACE **RIGHT** IN FRONT OF **OUR FRONT DOOR**!

THEN **FAT FREDDY** COMES ALONG AND STEPS IN IT AND **TRACKS** IT ALL OVER THE **APARTMENT** AND THEN HE GETS BEAT UP BY FREEWHEELIN' FRANKLIN AND **PHINEAS** AND THEN HE **FORGETS** TO FEED ME IN ALL THE CONFUSION!

THIS PRACTICE MUST BE HALTED.

I'LL MAKE A SMALL **WATER** BOMB OUT OF A **PLASTIC SACK**!

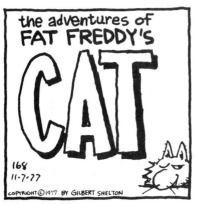

the adventures of
FAT FREDDY's
CAT

WHERE ARE **YOU** GOING?

I ALWAYS SPLIT FOR NEW YEAR'S!

EVERY YEAR, THE FREAK BROTHERS THROW A HUGE PARTY AND INVITE LOTS OF PEOPLE AND HAVE TONS OF THINGS TO EAT AND DRINK!

WHY ARE YOU LEAVING? THAT SOUNDS LIKE LOADS OF FUN!

OH, I DON'T MIND THE PARTY ITSELF...

...BUT FAT FREDDY IS ALWAYS SO SICK THE NEXT DAY IT GIVES ME A **CONTACT HANGOVER!**

TIME TO DECORATE THE APARTMENT FOR **HALLOWEEN!**

PHOOEY! ALL WE HAVE IS **CHRISTMAS** TYPE STUFF!

HERE'S SOME BLACK SHOE POLISH! I COULD MAKE **YOU** INTO A **WITCH'S CAT!**

HOW ABOUT **DYEING YOU ORANGE** AND YOU COULD BE A **GIANT PUMPKIN?**

the adventures of
FAT FREDDY's
CAT

I HEAR CLANKING NOISES IN THE KITCHEN!

JUST AS I'D HOPED! IT'S FAT FREDDY **COOKING** SOMETHING!

PERHAPS IT'S A DELICIOUS **STEW**, FULL OF PIECES OF TASTY **BEEF**!

...OR MAYBE A CAULDRON OF **CHICKEN SOUP**, OR ELSE A POT OF **CHILI**, OR MAYBE...

BOILING YOUR SOCKS?

YEAH, IT'S THE ONLY WAY I CAN GET TH' THINGS **CLEAN**!

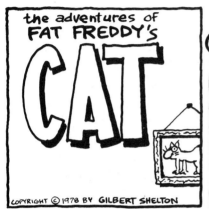

the adventures of
FAT FREDDY'S
CAT

MAY WE GO PLAY IN THE STREET, UNCLE F.?

THAT'S VERY RISKY! YOU MIGHT RUN INTO A **DIMENSIONAL TRANSMOGRIFIER!**

WHAT'S **THAT**?

SOME PEOPLE CALL THEM "CARS" AND "TRUCKS"; I CALL THEM <u>DIMENSIONAL TRANSMOGRIFIERS</u>...

...BECAUSE THEY CHANGE **THREE**-DIMENSIONAL **CATS** INTO **TWO**-DIMENSIONAL ONES!

the adventures of
FAT FREDDY'S
CAT

FAT FREDDY !!
SOMEONE CRAPPED
IN THE KITCHEN
SINK AGAIN!

...AND THERE
GOES A VERY
GUILTY-
LOOKING
CAT!

ZIP

WHERE IS HE HIDING!?

HE'S IN HERE SOME-
WHERE!

I'LL LOOK IN
THE CLOSET!

THE OLD "FUR COAT
TRICK" DOESN'T
WORK SO WELL
IN AN EMPTY
CLOSET!

BOOT!

the adventures of
FAT FREDDY'S
CAT
203   7·10·78

COPYRIGHT © 1978
BY GILBERT SHELTON

ASLEEP AGAIN...

HOW CAN CATS **SLEEP** SO MUCH? HE MUST BE **AWAKE** LESS THAN **TWO HOURS A DAY!**

YAWN! (STRETCH!)

FRANKLY, IT'S **NOT** SO DIFFICULT **NOWADAYS...**

...BUT I DON'T KNOW **HOW** I DID IT BEFORE FAT FREDDY GOT HIS **PRESCRIPTION** FOR **VALIUM!**

the adventures of FAT FREDDY's CAT

181 2·6·78

COPYRIGHT© 1978 BY GILBERT SHELTON

BIG PARTY LAST NIGHT!

I'LL JUST TAKE A LOOK AROUND AND SEE IF ANYONE DROPPED ANY **GOODIES!**

FOUR PIECES OF SALAMI AND A PIECE OF KENTUCKY FRIED CHICKEN WING! **NOT BAD!**

...BUT **HERE'S** ONE OF MY **FAVORITE** THINGS OF **ALL!**

CLAM DIP EMBELLISHED WITH **COCKROACHES!** THEY MUST HAVE MADE THIS UP **ESPECIALLY** FOR **ME!**

YOW!) SCREAM!

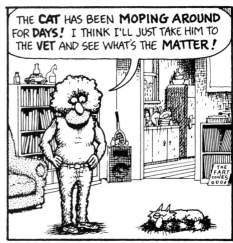

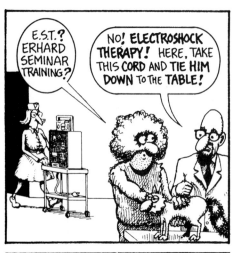

HOWEVER, IN HIS HASTE THE GOOD DOCTOR INSERTS THE TWO PLUGS IN THE WRONG HOLES.

THAT'S WHAT'S KNOWN AS "THE COVER-UP!"

THE END

the adventures of
FAT FREDDY'S
CAT

WORKERS OF THE WORLD UNITE

AAAARRRRGHHH!

YOU CAN'T TALK TO ME LIKE THAT!

I QUIT!

OUT! OUT! OUT! AND DON'T EVER COME **BACK!**

(SIGH!) FIRED AGAIN!

I JUST CANNOT REMEMBER **NOT** TO **SHIT** ON FAT FREDDY'S **PILLOW** WHEN IT'S TOO COLD TO GO **OUTSIDE!**

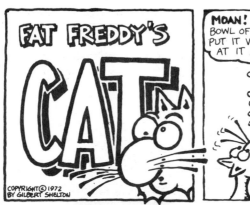

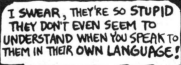

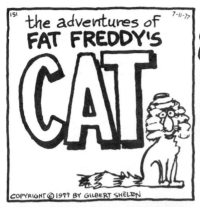

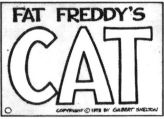

the adventures of
FAT FREDDY'S
CAT

COPYRIGHT © 1980
BY GILBERT SHELTON

I DON'T **LIKE** ALL THESE **FLIES** BUZZING AROUND!

WELL, YOU PICK OUT THE ONES YOU **LIKE** AND I'LL **KILL** THE REST! HA HA HA!

SERIOUSLY, GUYS, WE NEED TO PUT UP ONE OF THESE ROLLS OF **FLYPAPER**!

THE NEXT DAY:

(YAWN!) **NOON** ALREADY? I MUST GO INTO THE **KITCHEN** AND SEE HOW MANY **FLIES** THE **FLYPAPER** HAS CAUGHT!

!!

STOP **LAUGHING**, YOU FAT FOOL, AND COME **CUT ME LOOSE**!

the adventures of
FAT FREDDY'S
CAT

179 1-23-78
COPYRIGHT © 1978 BY GILBERT SHELTON

OH BOY! FAT FREDDY GOT A NEW CARTON OF MILK AND WENT AWAY WITHOUT PUTTING IT IN THE REFRIGERATOR!

CLUNK!

SPLOOT!

IT WAS A LOT EASIER TO OPEN BEFORE THEY CHANGED FROM BOTTLES TO CARTONS!

the adventures of
FAT FREDDY'S

CAT

NEW ELECTRIC HAIR DRYER!

YOU WANNA **SEE** HOW IT **WORKS**?

LOOK! THE **CAT** DOESN'T KNOW WHAT TO **THINK** OF IT!

WHIRRRRRR

TASTE INTERGALACTIC DEATH RAY, VILE ALIEN! ZAP! ZAP! ZAP!

WHIRRRRRR

!!?

YOU CAN COME OUT, KITTY! IT'S **HARMLESS!** I PROMISE!

HA HA HA!

♪♫

?

CLICK

WHIRRRRRR

WHAT ARE YOU **DOING?** HEY, DON'T PLAY WITH MY **HAIR DRYER!**

GET AWAY FROM HERE WITH THAT THING! IT'S **DANGEROUS!**

I THOUGHT YOU SAID IT WAS **HARMLESS!**

WHIRRRR

NO! NO! PUT IT **DOWN!** PUT IT **DOWN! PLEASE!**

WHIRRRRRR

OH! OKAY!

MORAL:

DON'T **MUCK AROUND** WITH **FAT FREDDY'S CAT!**

the adventures of
FAT FREDDY's

CAT

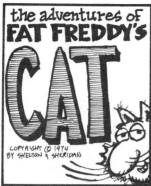

the adventures of
FAT FREDDY'S
CAT

COPYRIGHT © 1974
BY SHELTON & SHERIDAN

FAT FREDDY DOESN'T KNOW I'M A **STOWAWAY** IN THE BACK OF THE **VAN!**

IT'S EASY ENOUGH TO HIDE UNDER THIS HUGE PILE OF JUNK!

IT HAS **ALL** THE **COMFORTS** OF **HOME**...

...EXCEPT A "**SANDBOX!**"

BOY, IS FAT FREDDY GONNA BE SURPRISED WHEN HE CRAWLS INTO HIS **BEDROLL!**

the adventures of **FAT FREDDY'S** **CAT**

COPYRIGHT © 1979 BY GILBERT SHELTON

TALL TOAD BEER

Z

(YAWN) (STRETCH) THAT WAS A RESTFUL LITTLE NAP! NOW I THINK I'LL TAKE A **SNACK** BREAK!

GOOD GRIEF! WHAT IN THE **WORLD** IS **THAT**?

OUT! OUT! OUT!

AND DON'T COME **BACK** UNTIL YOU SMELL NICE AGAIN!

NOW I KNOW BETTER THAN TO SLEEP IN FAT FREDDY'S **DIRTY SOCK** COLLECTION!